SHALL WE
JOIN THE MEN?

With best wishes
Oliver Preston

SHALL WE JOIN THE MEN?

TEN YEARS OF CARTOONS FROM THE FIELD AND ELSEWHERE

OLIVER PRESTON

BEVERSTON PRESS

For Vivien, Amber and Otto.

First published in Great Britain in 2005 by

BEVERSTON PRESS

Tetbury, Glos GL8 8TT

British Library cataloguing in Publication Data
A catalogue record for this title is available from The British Library

ISBN 0 9549936 0 8

Design by homercreative 0121 605 0103

I DON'T UNDERSTAND WHY
AFTER THE MONEY ONE SPENDS....

....SEEING A SURGEON....

....BUYING A BOOB JOB....

....HAVING A TUCK....

....A NIP IN THE WAIST....

....AND DOING ONE'S NOSE....

....ENLARGING ONE'S LIPS....

....ON BEAUTIFUL EYES....

....LIFTING ONE'S CHIN...

....AND DOING ONE'S HAIR....

....AND AFTER ALL THAT TROUBLE....

...MEN STILL THINK YOU'RE STUPID!

INTRODUCTION

"When you talk about cartoons you look up, when you talk about the city, you look down," a man commented to me in November 1995. The following Monday I left banking to pursue a career as a full-time cartoonist. **Shall We Join The Men?** is a selection of 10 years of my work.

Britain has a wonderful heritage of over 300 years of cartoons and caricature but there is still no set career path for progressing in this genre of art. As such many cartoonists are self taught. I have always considered the best cartoons to be 50% idea and 50% drawing - not always an easy balance to achieve. People often frustratingly ask, 'So, do you think up the captions as well?', something that seems to me to be a pre-requisite for being a cartoonist! My own cartoon apprenticeship, as a child, was soaking up the masters of cartooning from the last century: Bateman's humour of the embarrassment, Ffolkes' fanfares, Thelwell's countryside and the macabre world of Charles Addams' New Yorker cartoons. Later I would discover Gillray, Rowlandson and Cruikshank and the golden ages of caricature and Punch, and as a teenager, caricaturing at school, and drawing for college and university magazines. In 1986 a move into banking saw me collecting cartoons, rather than drawing them.

Since 1996 I have been fortunate to draw for The Field Magazine which was founded in 1853, and have editor Jonathan Young, and Rebecca Hawtrey, the art editor, to thank for publishing my drawings. **Shall We Join The Men?** has a wide splattering of dilettantes, languid lovelies and determined dogs, but over the past decade I have also tried to observe some of the vagaries of town versus country living: the rolling out of urbanisation into the countryside, the ever upward spiral of property prices, the pains of the long distance commuter and the decline of rural communities: the obfuscation of farming, and field sports in particular. Charles Addams' black and white wash cartoons of the macabre have always been an enduring influence on my drawing so inevitably a seam of dark humour features throughout.

Today clients are more demanding than ever in the turnaround time for cartoons, but the arrival of scanners, artwork editing software, the internet, websites and digital printing has greatly eased the routine of this cartoonist. A cartoon will often convey more to an onlooker than can ever be expressed in words, but today the opportunities for press publication become fewer and fewer. A full-page cartoon in the 1997 Valentine's Week issue of Punch Magazine (opposite) for me heralded new opportunities but sadly Punch ceased publication soon after; in newspapers and magazines today, photographers reign at the expense of the illustrators and cartoonists.

From 2005 I will have been a cartoonist for longer than I worked in the City of London; the variety of work, the observation of society, the developing of skills, the laughter and friends, and most of all the enjoyment of my growing family in the beautiful surroundings of the Cotswolds make it all worthwhile.

OLIVER PRESTON

June 2005

"All my sons are pilots, except Mickey who's just gone into the church."

"Come on Billy, they're playing our tune."

"Owing to his Lordship's recent acrimonious divorce, the hall is now open at half price."

"At least you saved the cat."

"Please don't talk while I'm interrupting."

"Help!"

"It's a goal!"

"Very nice, but is there room to swing a cat?"

"Any dead?"

"First class?"

"Can you let me out? I need to do my business."

"Isn't this the video of how the cat got run over?"

"Looks like Sheriff Foyle's going for his gun."

"Now that the children have gone back to school,
the wife really looks forward to a bit of quality time with me."

"...and what's your wife's hobby?"

Penelope sensed one of Henry's faux-pas coming on.

"It's lovely to see your father again. He hasn't changed a bit!"

"When I started this journey I was a curate."

"Grab a seat."

And Noah seth "Sod the dodo's", and so it came to pass.

"At this rate Philip, we're not going to get there until after the last race."

OLIVER PRESTON

2005

"Since we moved to the country our quality of life has doubled."

"...and then he comes downstairs wearing plus fours and carrying a gun."

"Your New Year's resolutions, you fat, unfit, drunken, cigar-puffing, chocolate-scoffing, miserable old git."

"Shall we join the men?"

"*The traffic wardens around here are absolute bastards.*"

"Yo baby. I'm on the tube."

"Isn't that the ghastly couple we met skiing in Meribel?"

"Isn't that the ghastly couple we met last summer in Rock?"

"You don't think I invited you to Gstaad for the skiing?"

"This only happens when it's my turn to drive home."

"You might want to drink that before the rest of the grandchildren arrive."

The Absent Friend

Feathered Family

"Has anything been moved?"

"The old trout's on the other line."

"It's clues we're fishing for. Constable."

"It's his superior than thou attitude that gets me."

"Best property deal he ever did."

Incapability O'Brien lacked the precision of his English cousin.

"We're only keeping it all going for the sake of the children."

"Your husband was obscenely rich - until he took up polo."

*"My wife tells me that living here during the week
is a small price to pay for the comforts of the country."*

Breeds apart.

"I'm afraid the house has gone to the dogs"

"He'll see you in a minute."

"Is that maintenance? There's an employee blocking my view."

"I'm glad we had Mother cremated. It's as if she's still with us."

"Hugh was a popular man..."

"Going hunting?"

"...and did you pack the bags yourself?"

"He's also our MP."

"No buts... your father gave up smoking in his thirties."

"It's the new five pounds congestion charge for entering our village."

"I don't know about the antis, but it'll certainly confuse the fox."

"Would you like me to have a go?"

"You've had a lovely day, don't spoil it."

*"Very nice darling, but I think we both know
I'm worth more than a standard tariff."*

"It's only me!"

"Cremation or burial or would he prefer a surprise?"

"Are you thinking what I'm thinking?"

"Business is down 50% since Cartwright here merged
our last two remaining clients together."

*"Sometimes I think you only married me
for my father's grouse moor."*

"I'm sure she would have got in, had the exam
been called something a little more upmarket."

"It needs shortening."

"It's the waterboard. They want to sell us some electricity."

"Good Mourning!"

"That's showbiz for you."

"Women's orgasms? You'll find them under fiction."

"One of the perks of the chairman's job is this fantastic view."

ACKNOWLEDGMENTS

Illustration Acknowledgments:

1, 3, 9, 11, 19, 22, 23, 25, 28, 29, 31, 32, 33, 34, 36, 37, 38, 39, 40, 41, 42, 43, 44, 45, 46, 47, 49, 50, 51, 54, 55, 56, 57, 58, 60, 61, 63, 65, 71, 72, 76, 77, 78, 79, 81, 82, 83, 88, 90, 91
The Field Magazine. 1996-2005

5, Liquid Limericks. 2001

52, 53 The Countryside Alliance. 1998, 1999

6, Punch Magazine. 1997

By the same author

With Alistair Sampson

Liquid Limericks (2001) Robson Books
Larder Limericks (2004) Robson Books

Firstly many thanks to Brian Homer, Sue Race and Jim Deaves for advising me and producing the book. Jonathan Young, Rebecca Hawtrey and their team at The Field Magazine where many of these cartoons were first published. Peter Burdett for reassuring me that there was another career beyond banking, and the wonderful Norma Crownshaw, Maggie Heath and Pat Huntley for their enduring support. My parents Nick and Elsbeth Preston, whose extensive humour continues to provide sounding boards for ideas and drawings, and who introduced me to cartoons early in life. More thanks than ever to Vivien and Amber the inspirational women in my life.